Date Due

D1212734

the
practically
complete
guide to
almost real
musical
instruments
for nearly
everyone

by HARVEY RUDOFF

the practically complete guide to almost real musical instruments for nearly everyone

THE AUTHOR **HARVEY RUDOFF**

LERNER PUBLICATIONS COMPANY
4377 Minneapolis, Minnesota

CONTENTS

the lurk

The Lurk fits inside your piano,
It doesn't make noise;
It just enjoys
The inside of the piano.

the blomp

They say that when the sun goes down,
That's when the Blomp walks into town
And it whistles till the break of day.
Anyway, that's what they say.
I've heard that when the skies are dark
The Blomp strolls gaily through the park
And whistles tunes just like a bird.
Anyway, that's what I've heard.
Now, if some black and spooky night
You step outside to see this sight,
The Blomp will eat your shoes and hat.
Nobody ever tells you that.

The Dozer plays but once a year,
And never in-between;
Even if the King demands,
Or even if the Queen.
Even if the Parliament
Takes it rather hard,
Even if the London Times
Calls out Scotland Yard.
Even if the British fleet
Sends an S.O.S.,
Even if the Prince of Wales
Begs it to say ''yes.''
They'd rather have the Dozer play
Music that is boring,
Than have to listen one more day
To its confounded snoring.

the dozer

the groanette

A Groanette makes you very proud
Because it plays so awfully loud;
    It doesn't whisper,
    Doesn't mumble.
    When it plays
    Buildings crumble.
Be the first one in your block
To give the neighborhood a shock;
    Take the Groanette
    In your hand,
    And make your town
    A No-Man's Land.

If your skill should be disputed,
Play a tone that's softly muted;
    (Even this
    Should be enough
    To blow up schools
    And stores and stuff.)
While your neighbors rub their eyes
The dust and smoke begin to rise
    In such a pretty
    Mushroom cloud;
    I told you
    It would make you proud.

the six-wheeled furble

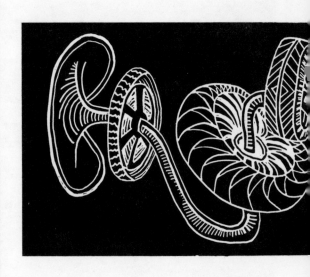

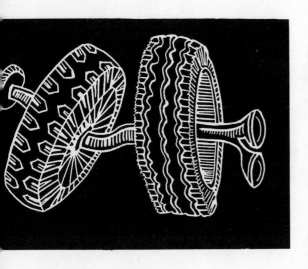

There are seven tires
On the Six-Wheeled Furble,
But there's a reason for that.
The extra one's there
For use as a spare,
Just in case of A ♭ .

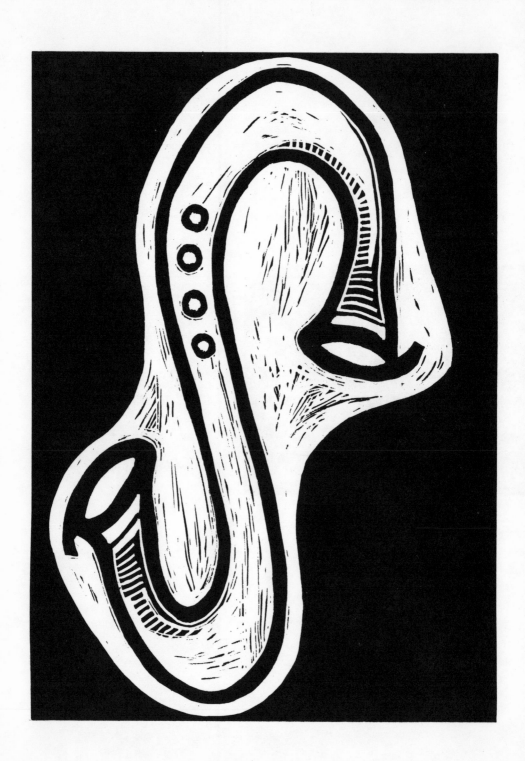

ou want to know
ich end to blow,
n't rant and rave and shout.
st try, my friend,
e opposite end
m the end the sound comes out.
he end with the sound
nnot be found,
ugh you've looked for it high and low,
ve you tried
e opposite side
the end in which you blow?

the double honk

the turnabout

The Turnabout is really bold;
Don't let it stump or faze you.
Sit and take it with a smile
As it gently plays you.

the contragump

I can't agree with those who say
The Contragump is hard to play.
I didn't find it hard at all,
But then, I'm over 12 feet tall.

the musical scale

The Musical Scale
As you can see,
Has nothing to do
With Do - Re - Mi.
It weighs all the notes,
Whatever their sound,
And sells them for only
A dollar a pound.
The notes are delicious,
Won't you have a few?
The sweet ones are good;
The sour ones, too.
Fill up your pockets
Some afternoon,
And all the way home
You can carry a tune.

the snaxophone

The principles on which it's based
Are really nothing new,
First, every note in perfect taste,
And second, nuts to you.

The three-holed Savanah
Is like a banana.
Just pick one up and feel it.
Now hold it just so,
Get ready to blow
—Not that way, my friend.
First peel it.

the three-holed savanah

22

Horns that play with dulcet tones
Are not a bit like Bofflebones,
And those that play in alto clef
Or play so loud they drive you deaf,
Or play in keys like E or F,
— They don't play like Bofflebones.
Horns that play in semitones
Are not at all like Bofflebones,
And those that play with brassy sounds
Or play a scale by leaps and bounds,
Or play caprices, jigs and rounds,
— They don't play like Bofflebones.
Yes, a Bofflebone is quite unique;
It only plays — guess —
Hide-and-Seek.

the bofflebone

the vendorina

A button for treble,
A button for bass,
One for each line
And one for each space.
A button for fast,
A button for slow,
A button for stop
And a button for go.
Buttons for rhythm,
Buttons for tone,
Buttons in bunches
And buttons alone.
But the absolute very best
Button of all,
Is the one that you press
For a malted milk ball.

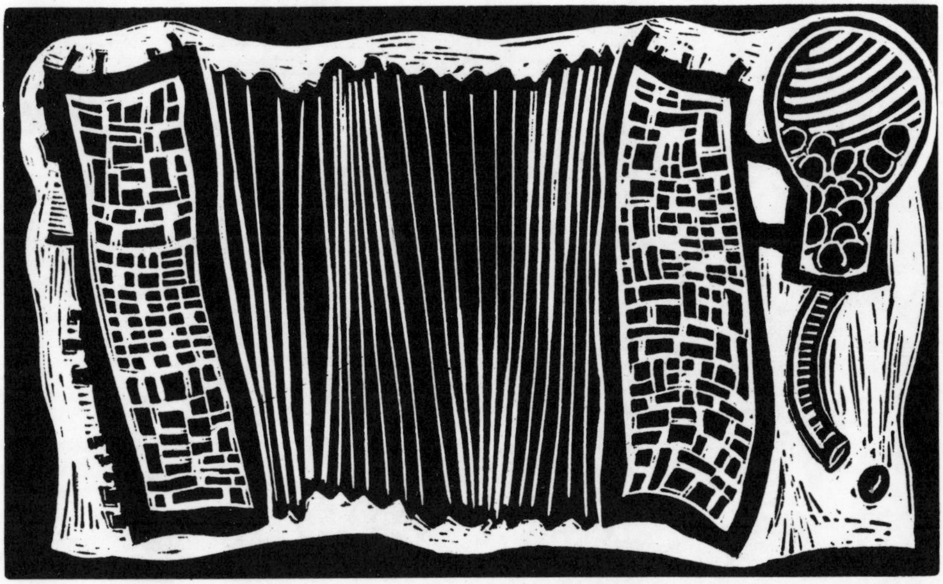

Upon the Gorse
Do not depend;
It refuses to play
All the way to the end.
What kind of person
Would play on the Gorse?
The answer is simple:
I do, of

the gorse

Drop a penny in the slot,
Turn the crank with all you've got;
Grab the handle, shift the gear,
Push the pedal, shout ''All Clear!''
    Now, in order
    To begin,
    Put another
    Penny in.
Spin the wheel to the right,
Twist the knob until it's tight;
Press the button, hold her steady,
Flick the switch. You're almost ready!
    Now, in order
    To commence,
    Please deposit
    Fifty cents.
Watch the dial, wind the spring,
Keep your eye on everything;
Set the timer, check the straps,
Fasten clips and snap the snaps.
    Here we go!
    —Or we will,
    If you'll insert
    A dollar bill.
Nothing more is needed now.
Start to play and
          — HOLY COW!
It's not my fault it won't begin,
I thought you had plugged it in!

the musivac 707

Mr. Rudoff lives quietly, or as quietly as possible, with his wife and 4 children in Denver, Colorado. Between summer vacations, he teaches band and orchestra in a junior high school in Denver. He has also taught for several years on the elementary level, where he made many friends, most of whom were in the third grade.

"There is a great deal to be said for having friends in the third grade," says Mr. Rudoff. "They will never turn against you. The only time they raise a hand to the teacher is when they have to go to the bathroom. They are very dependable."

When he is not teaching school, Mr. Rudoff is thirty-one years old and collects rocks. He has one rock that he found on a camping trip that is very pretty, and another that is not too bad looking. He believes the kaleidoscope is one of the ten greatest inventions in the world (followed closely by ice cream and the bubble pipe).

He is a graduate of Northwestern University (1950-59), and his humorous poems, drawings and articles appear frequently in leading music magazines. He played solo clarinet for 2 years with the 76th Army Band in Paris, France.

Having carved the linoleum blocks from which the drawings in this book were printed, he insists that one day he will carve a totem pole. "All I need," says his wife, "is a totem pole."